LISTEN, RABBIT

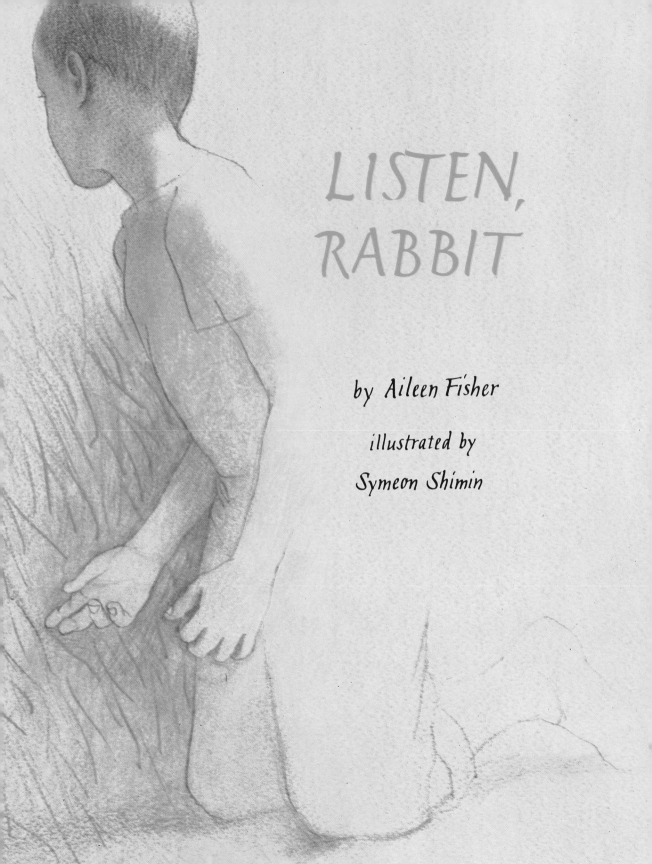

LISTEN, RABBIT

by Aileen Fisher

illustrated by
Symeon Shimin

THOMAS Y. CROWELL COMPANY, NEW YORK

By the Author

Going Barefoot

Where Does Everyone Go?

Like Nothing at All

I Like Weather

Listen, Rabbit

In the Middle of the Night

Arbor Day

Library of Congress Catalog Card No. 64-10860

ISBN: 0-690-49591-9
       0-690-49592-7 (LB)

Published in Canada by Fitzhenry & Whiteside Limited, Toronto

6 7 8 9 10

LISTEN, RABBIT

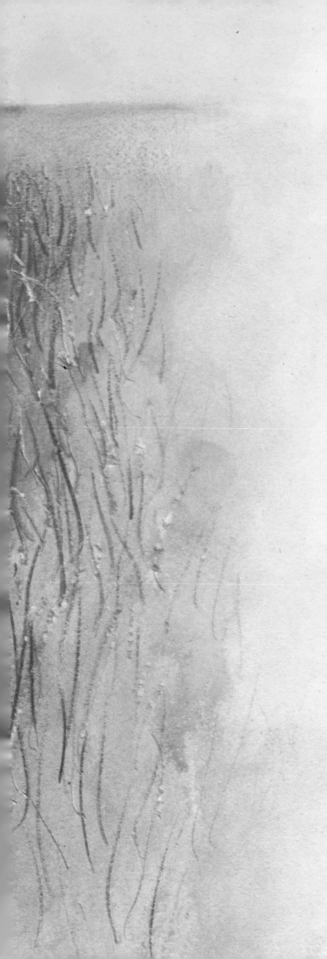

I saw him first
when the sun went down
in the summer sky
at the edge of town
where grass grew green
and the path grew brown.

I couldn't tell
what he was at all
when I saw him first,
sort of halfway small,
sort of halfway grown,
near a gray old stone
in the field, alone.

Then I saw his ears
standing rabbit tall!

I stood as still
as a maple tree
and I looked at him
and he looked at me . . .
with only one eye
that I could see,
bulging out
on the side of his head.

"Nice little rabbit,"
I softly said
inside myself,
though I hoped he'd hear
with two long ears
standing up so near
and my thoughts so clear.

My heart went thump!
And do you know why?
'Cause I hoped that maybe
as time went by
the rabbit and I
(if he felt like *me*)
could have each other
for company.

I didn't have a puppy.
I didn't have a mouse.

My sister had kittens
all over the house
and a tabby-striped cat
in a tabby-striped blouse,
and Mother kept saying,
"A motherly cat
with umpteen kittens
is plenty. That's *that*."

I didn't have a pony.
I didn't have a horse.

There wasn't much room
at our house, of course.
And Father kept saying,
"With a motherly cat
and all those kittens
to pet and pat
we've more than enough
. . . and that is *that*."

But it *wasn't* enough,
and I watched the rabbit
and hoped some day
it would let me nab it.

I watched as still
as a windless tree,
and that was exceedingly still
. . . for me.

The rabbit sat still
where the light was dim,
but that was a rabbity habit
. . . for him.

His ears stood tall
and his ears stood proud,
pointing straight up
at a sunset cloud,
and I said softly
(not quite out loud):

    "Listen, rabbit,
    with such tall ears
    you hear more
    than *anyone* hears.

"With two antennae
sticking up high
bringing you news
of earth and sky,
maybe you even
hear harebells ringing,
dogwood barking,
and larkspur singing!"

His nose didn't even
twitch or wiggle,
so I went on
with a halfway giggle:

"Listen, rabbit,
do you know what *I'd* do
if I had antennae ears
like you?

"I'd hop, hop, hop
to a candy shop
and listen
to every last lolliPOP!"

His whiskers didn't
so much as flicker,
and I didn't move
or even snicker,
hoping that way
to make friends quicker.

But we didn't make friends
that day because
my sister came running
(she always does),
running and calling,
calling and waving,
waving and other such
loud behaving.

Leap! went my rabbit
down the meadow
past a burrow,
over a furrow,
through a shadow,
under some bushes
near a billow
of bending grass
and a weeping willow.

Leap! Hop!
Jump and away!
Until he was lost
in the dusky hay.

"You've got to come home,"
my sister said.
(She only had kittens
inside her head.)

On the way home
I thought about ears . . .
the hundreds of things
a cottontail hears
probably,
possibly,
liker than not
that *we* never know
are Whether or What:

Sound of spiders taking a walk,
sound of aphids sucking a stalk,
sound of beetles dodging a hawk,
sound of fireflies talking their talk.

I picked up a stick
and thought about eyes,
thought how my rabbit
was certainly wise
to grow his eyes
on the *sides* instead
of right up front
on his little fur head,

Thought how my rabbit
was not a dunce
to look more directions
than one, at once . . .
with so many enemies
waiting to snatch him,
race him, chase him,
worry and catch him!

I kicked at a stone
and thought about feet,
thought how a rabbit's
were certainly neat—
rompy and stompy
and springy and fleet,
hoppy and ploppy
and hard to beat . . .

My sister said, "*What*
are you blinking about,
dreaming and scheming
and thinking about?"

"Nothing," I said . . .
and my thoughts winked out
like a flick of foam.

And I raced her home.

And then for a week
I didn't see him.

Poor little rabbit
I'd hate to *be* him
when the sun goes pale
and under a veil
and we have thunder
and rain and hail.

Standing at the window,
looking at the rain
weeping down the eye
of the windowpane,
I tried to picture
how it would be
living out there
near a wet old tree . . .
like the rabbit
who nearly belonged to me.

Where did he scrunch
when the rain bounced by?
What about lunch
and clover to munch
for dinner and brunch?
And did he keep dry?

The next time I saw him
he was just a Hop
at the edge of the meadow.
Flippity-flop
my rabbit sprang off
and never did stop,
though I brought him a bun
and a carrot top.

Leap! Jump!
Hop and away!
So we didn't make friends
that day.

And then it was time
for school again.
Mornings and evenings
turned cool again,
and there wasn't much chance
to think of rabbits
or walk through places
with rabbity habits.

But once
on a Saturday morning, early,
when the sky was pink
and mother-of-pearly
and the grass
was silvery-wet and yellow,
I saw my hoppery rabbit fellow
under a tree.
And he saw me.

We looked at each other
a long, long while.

He had a face
that couldn't smile.
I had a face
that could smile a lot,
but I thought, "For a while
I'd better not . . .

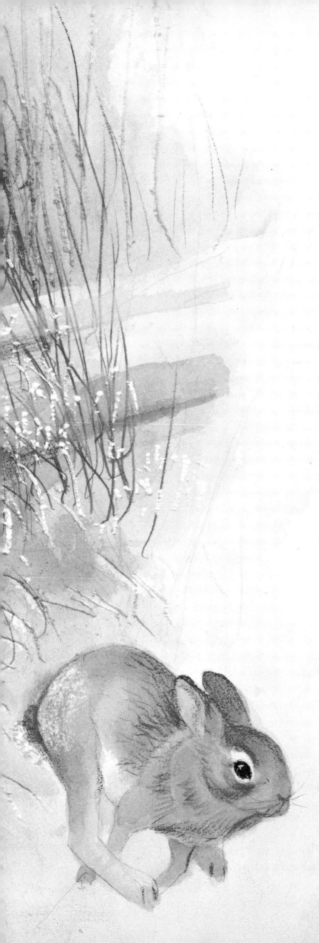

better not move
a single muscle
or make a rustle
or be in a hustle."

His ears stood high
with the insides pink
and I urged him, "*Try*
to hear what I think
about being friends
before autumn ends."
But his round black eye
didn't even blink.

And then a dog
gave a nearby yip,
and my rabbit was gone
with a flip and a zip
into the bushes across the way,
into the brush
where the Tangles stay.

And we didn't make friends
that day.

I stood one night
(when the moon was bright)
out in the yard
and thought real hard
of wildwood rabbits
with moonlight habits:

I never had seen
but I'd heard it said
that nary a cottontail
lies abed
when the eye of the moon
is big and bright.

He's out on his toes
in the moonstruck night,
dancing, prancing,
leaping, hopping,
jumping, thumping,
ears a-flopping.

So I sent a thought
through the magic air:

> "Listen, rabbit,
> are *you* out there
> with stars in your eyes
> and a moon to wear
> and feet that go leaping
> everywhere?"

I couldn't go see
because, instead,
I'm always having
to go to bed!
So I went upstairs
and switched the light . . .
and we didn't make friends
that night.

In fall when the wind
raced down the hill
and nothing in all
the world was still,
I looked for my bunny
grayish brown
and hoped he flattened
his ears both down,

For how could a rabbit
with ears up tall,
picking up noises
big and small . . .
how could he hear
himself think at all
with a cry
in the sky
and a push
and a swoosh
and a snap, rap, tap
in the tree,
in the bush,
and a sway
in the hay
and a scare
in the air
and a creak, squeak, tweak
where the boughs
rubbed bare?

I saw where he sat . . .
near a pile of boulders,
his ears down flat
on his hunched–up shoulders,

And he didn't hear
as I crept his way,
in the swish and sway
of the trees and hay,
but he must have seen
with his bulging eye
the bigness of me
as I slipped by
the place where a bush
and boulder met . . .

So we didn't make friends
quite *yet!*

And then one morning,
what do you know?
When I got up
a blanket of snow
covered the world
from top to toe.

I had to gasp,
I had to blink
when I thought of
what-would-my-rabbit-think?

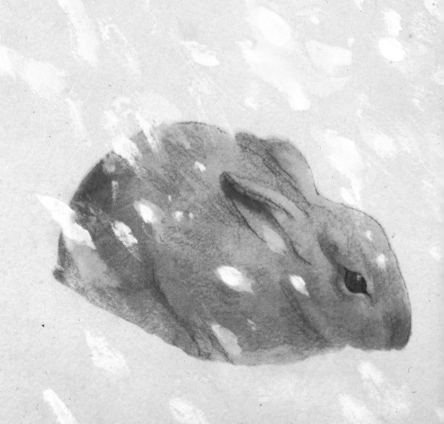

His ears knew all about
pine trees humming,
aspens quaking,
west wind strumming,
hound dogs yapping,
flickers drumming,
but how could they know about
snowflakes coming?

I thought of him there
in the snowy air,
a summer old
and the year turned cold:

"Listen, rabbit . . .
I'd like to know
can you hear the quiet
of windless snow
falling like star dust
ashy white,
falling like feathers,
fluffy, light?

"Listen, rabbit . . .
you mustn't mind
when you look around
at the snow and find
all your tracks
on your trail, behind!"

My sister and I
One after-school
went to slide on the ice
of the meadow pool,
and I saw my rabbit's
tracks by dozens
(though maybe a few
belonged to cousins).
I saw his tracks
and I said, "How *funny*
bunny tracks go
when a bunny is runny!
The hind feet show
in front of the *front*
on the telltale snow.
Well, what do you know!"

I didn't expect,
with my sister along
talking and singing
a snatch of song,
to see my rabbit.

I wasn't wrong.

Somewhere safe
he was hidden away . . .
so we didn't make friends
that day.

Snow kept falling
and wild winds blew,
and I skied and skated . . .
and before I knew,
peepers were peeping
and birds were cheeping
and ladybugs creeping
and winter was through!

One Saturday morning
I went for an outing
to see how much
of the world was sprouting
and if my rabbit
was roundabouting.

I heard the frogs,
mosquitoes, and bees,
birds on the wires
and birds in the trees . . .
but rabbits aren't noted
for sounds like these,
so I had to look,
and at last I spied him—
with bursting buds
of a bush beside him.

His coat looked frumpled
and weather-rumpled,
and when I came near
for him to hear
how I hoped it would be
with him and me,
he looked *much bigger*
and full of vigor . . .

Hop! Jump!
to a woodsy glen.
So we didn't make friends again.

. . . And then
on a day that was bright
as shined-up glass
I found a secret
down in the grass,
so hidden a person
might pass and pass
and never once know.
I found it, though . . .
hidden and grassy
and cupped and low.

Blow carefully,
wind of spring!
Down in the grass
is a wonderful thing . . .

Down in the grass
in a fur-lined nest
are cottontail babies
still undressed,
eyes still closed,
and new and pink . . .
five little cottontails,
what do you think!

Blow carefully,
wind of spring!
Watch the kind
of weather you bring.
Only a week
and new fur coats
will rumple around
the bunnies' throats,
eyes will open,
and tails will show . . .
five little cottontails,
what do you know!

"Listen, rabbit!"
I laughed and cried,
feeling all shiny
and warm inside.
"What a wonderful
secret surprise I've spied,
what a wonderful secret
for you to hide."

I hadn't a pony
or pup
to pet,

I hadn't a rabbit
exactly, yet,

But I
had a nest
like a fur-lined cup

And *five baby rabbits*
to watch grow up!